AWARD PUBLICATIONS – LONDON

Tinker wants to know

LUCIENNE ERVILLE - MARCEL MARLIER

Tinker was asleep
in the workbasket,
on a lovely
piece of soft,
pale blue knitting. He opened
one eye, then another... gave
a sleepy purr and thought about getting washed.
But he fell asleep again and began dreaming.

Suddenly, "Woof! Woof!" Tinker woke up with a start. It was Rusty his little friend. Without waiting to get tidy, Tinker dashed out to join him.

Rusty looked at him.

"Goodness, Tinker, you do look a mess! You haven't even combed your whiskers!"

"It's all very well for you dogs," Tinker said, crossly. "Other people brush you and bath you and polish you up. We cats have to do it all for ourselves!"

But Tinker did not really envy Rusty He thought that burying bones and wagging your tail were a bit stupid.

All the same, Tinker decided to tidy up before they went out. He rubbed the backs of his ears, licked himself and soon looked neat as a new pin. Rusty watched admiringly.

That morning the weather was dull, but Rusty had an idea.
"Come on, Tinker, let's play the Cloud Game!"
Off they went and settled on the mossy garden wall.

They gazed up at the sky.

"What do you think that looks like?" asked Rusty

"It looks like a cloud," said Tinker, puzzled.

Rusty did not bother to explain, but pointed to another cloud.

"I think that one looks like a tom-cat."

Suddenly Tinker understood.

"Or a big ball of grey wool!" he shouted.

The next cloud was a very, very long one.

"That's a marrow-bone," said Tinker. "Or maybe it's one of those stretched-out dogs!" That was what he called the little dachshund who lived next-door.

Rusty laughed and wagged his tail faster and faster.

Suddenly he remembered the strange news he had heard when he was in the village. "Listen, Tinker! I was talking to old Ben and he told me that he had heard there was a school for dogs! Apparently you can learn to be a guard dog or a hunting dog or a guide dog. Ben even said you could learn to be a circus dog and dance about wearing a skirt!" Tinker was amazed! Schools for dogs!

"But Rusty you won't leave me to go to school, will you?"

"Of course not," said Rusty "I'd much rather stay at home and play with you!"

"Do you suppose they have Cat Schools, too?" asked Tinker with interest. He could picture himself wearing big glasses and reading clever books.

"I don't know. Ben didn't say anything about them."

They had had enough of the Cloud
Game for one day, so they trotted
off past the big bed of dahlias.
"Aren't they pretty?" said Tinker.
"Do dahlias live for a long time?"
The Apple Tree, who had over-
heard, reassured him.
"They stay beautiful for weeks!"
"Thank you! I am glad," cried
Tinker, happily.

The goldfish pool was covered with waterlilies. Freddy the frog was dozing on a big leaf and all the pond was quiet. But suddenly a goldfish popped up between the leaves, and then another and another.

"Hello! Hello! Hello!"
Rusty and Tinker thought how lucky they were to have so many friends in the garden.

On their way to visit the Old Oak Tree, they met Howard the Hedgehog, who was sitting down and looking very tired.

"Oh, I've been working so hard! But now my winter house is nearly finished. Autumn is coming, you see..."

"What's autumn?" asked Tinker.

Howard laughed.

"Oh! Autumn is lots of things... grey days and rain and leaves turning red and falling off the trees. But the Old Oak Tree will explain it to you...

When it gets cold we hedgehogs go to sleep. We stay sound asleep for weeks and weeks and we have no idea what goes

on in the outside world."
Rusty and Tinker looked at him with big eyes. Fancy not eating or play-ing or seeing anybody

for so many months!

"Do you like sleeping all the time like that?" asked Tinker politely.

"Very much," replied Howard. "It's so practical, you see. We wake up all fit and fresh when the Spring comes. The only drawback is that we never see the snow, and people say it is so pretty. But excuse me. I must be off to finish my house."

The Old Oak Tree welcomed Rusty and Tinker in his deep, friendly voice.

"I am so glad to see you. The weather is beginning to get worse and I don't expect you will be coming this way very often."

Tinker was upset, and he stammered.

"I don't like it! Herbert said he was going to sleep all the time and your leaves were going to fall off!"

"It won't happen as quickly as that. But Howard is right all the same."

Just then a raindrop fell on Tinker's nose.

"Shelter under my leaves," said the Old Oak. "Bad weather's coming; we may have fog before very long."

"What's fog?" asked Tinker. He really did want to know everything!
"Fog? It is a cloud that comes down to the ground. Sometimes it's thin and light,

Tinker couldn't believe it. "Really you can't see anything? Not the house or the trees or Rusty?"

"No, really nothing. And you can get lost in it. It's better to stay at home in a fog or in a storm."

"What's a storm?" Tinker never gave up.

"It's lightning, making zig-zags in the sky, and great peals of thunder, like drums. But it's soon all over."

"I'm beginning to under-
stand things, Rusty! It
means we shall have to
play in the garden shed
among the flower pots!"

"And you can listen to the rain tapping
on the roof and windows!" added the
Old Oak.

Soon the rain stopped and Rusty and
Tinker thought they must go home.

"Come and see me when you can,"
said the Old Oak, rather sadly. "Then
I can tell you about the snow."

"What's snow?" asked Tinker, but
Rusty could not answer him. So there
was still something to learn.

"Aren't we lucky!" thought Tinker.
"Life is fun!"